Specials!

World War 1

Susan Merritt

Acknowledgements

© 2007 Folens Limited, on behalf of the author.

United Kingdom: Folens Publishers, Apex Business Centre, Boscombe Road, Dunstable, LU5 4RL.

Email: folens@folens.com

Ireland: Folens Publishers, Greenhills Road, Tallaght, Dublin 24.

Email: info@folens.ie

Poland: JUKA, ul. Renesansowa 38, Warsaw 01-905.

Editor: Janice Baiton   Illustrations: Tony Randell   Layout artists: Book Matrix, India

Cover design: Holbrook Design   Cover image: Corbis

First published 2007 by Folens Limited.

Every effort has been made to contact copyright holders of material used in this publication. If any copyright holder has been overlooked, we should be pleased to make any necessary arrangements.

British Library Cataloguing in Publication Data. A catalogue record for this publication is available from the British Library.

ISBN 978-1-85008-211-8

Contents

Introduction

Specials! History have been specifically written for teachers to use with students who may struggle with some of the skills and concepts needed for Key Stage 3 History. The titles are part of a wider series from Folens for use with lower ability students.

Each book in the series contains ten separate units covering the topics needed to complete the theme of the book. Each unit has one or more photocopiable resource pages and several activity sheets. This allows the teacher to work in different ways. The tasks are differentiated throughout the book and offer all students the opportunity to expand their skills. By using photocopiable writing frames and emphasising literacy skills, students will be able to access historical information more easily.

The teacher's page at the start of each unit gives guidance on the material and is laid out as follows.

Objectives
These are the main skills or knowledge to be learned.

Prior knowledge
This refers to the minimum skills or knowledge required by students to complete the tasks. As a rule, students should have a reading comprehension age of 6 to 9 years and should be working at levels 1 to 3. Some activity sheets are more challenging than others and teachers will need to select accordingly.

QCA and NC links; Scottish attainment targets; Northern Ireland PoS
All units link to the QCA Schemes of Work and to the NC for History at Key Stage 3. There are also links to the Scottish 5–14 guidelines and the Northern Ireland PoS.

Background
This provides additional information for the teacher, expanding on historical details or giving further information about the unit.

Starter activity
Since the units can be taught as a lesson, a warm-up activity focusing on an aspect of the unit is suggested.

Resource sheets and activity sheets
The resource sheets, which are often visual but may also be written, do not include tasks and can be used as stimulus for discussion. Related tasks are provided on the activity sheets.

Where necessary, keywords are included on the student pages. Other keywords are included on the teacher's page. These can be introduced to students at the teacher's discretion and depending on students' abilities.

Plenary
The teacher can use the suggestions here to recap on the main points covered or to reinforce a particular idea.

Assessment sheet
At the end of the book is an assessment sheet focusing on student progress. It can be used in different ways. A student can complete it as a self-assessment, while the teacher also completes one on each student's progress. They can then compare the two. This is useful in situations where the teacher or classroom assistant is working with one student. Alternatively, students can work in pairs to carry out peer assessments and then compare the outcomes with each other. Starting from a simple base that students can manage, the assessment sheet allows the student to discuss their own progress, to consider different points of view and to discuss how they might improve, thus enabling the teacher to see the work from the student's perspective.

Look out for other titles in the History series, which include:
- The Romans
- Medieval Britain 1066–1485
- Changing Britain 1485–1750
- Industrial Britain 1750–1900
- Britain in the 20th century
- Black peoples of the Americas
- Women and the vote
- The Holocaust

Teacher's notes

How did World War 1 start?

Objectives

- Understand that there were several long-term causes of the war
- Understand the importance of the alliance system
- Identify the event that triggered the war
- Be familiar with and use historical keywords

Prior knowledge

Students need to be aware that Europe at the start of 1914 was very different from today and that many of the countries that make up the continent now did not exist, or formed part of other empires.

QCA link

Unit 18 Twentieth-century conflicts

NC links

History skills 5a, 7a, 7d
Breadth of study 13, the two world wars

Scottish attainment targets

Environmental Studies – Society – People in the past
Strand – Change and continuity, cause and effect
Level E
Strand – People, events and societies of significance in the past
Level D
Level E

Northern Ireland PoS

Study Unit 4: The twentieth-century world, a) The impact of world war, World War I
Study Units 5 and 6: c) A significant era or turning point in history, the First World War

Background

In 1914, Europe was divided into two major alliance systems that were involved in a power struggle. These had evolved during the previous century and were designed to protect nations from invasion or aggression. Great Britain and France were in direct financial, industrial and colonial competition with Germany. Germany was very aggressive in its pursuit of power. This led to an arms race and tension in Europe and many believed that a war was inevitable. However, previous wars had always been relatively small and nobody could have predicted the scale of the war that was about to erupt.

Starter activity

Ask students 'Why do wars happen?' Encourage them to come up with as many possible causes as they can think of and ask them to explain how they came by these ideas. Students should be encouraged to refer to recent conflicts that they are familiar with. In this way, they will understand that there are often many causes of a war and that such causes are rarely simple.

Resource sheets and activity sheets

'World War 1' provides several keywords for this unit. Go through these with the class as it is important that the students are familiar with these terms as they occur throughout the topic.

'Why was Europe ready for a war? (1)' and '(2)' provide students with a simplified overview of the long-term causes of the war. Ask for two volunteers to take on the roles of King George V and Kaiser Wilhelm II as you read through the pages. In this way, the long-term causes appear like a petty argument and are therefore more accessible than a complicated chain of events between competing alliances.

In 'The long-term causes of the war', the students should consolidate this information into four simple causes.

In 'The short-term cause: the excuse for war!', the students should discover how the assassination of Archduke Franz Ferdinand was the trigger that set off a chain of events leading to total war. Students are given the opportunity to see how the alliance system made war inevitable.

Plenary

Keyword bingo: write all the keywords, the names of the two alliances and the main individuals on the board. Ask the students to create a grid with six boxes in it. Each student should choose six of these words and write one in each of the boxes in their grid. Then ask the students questions about the units that use these words as answers. The first student to cross out all their six words is the winner.

World War 1

World War 1 started in 1914 and lasted for four years until 1918. It is called a world war because so many different countries were involved. There had never been a war that had been quite so big before and nobody was prepared for how hard it was going to be. By the end of World War 1, over eight million people had been killed.

The first question that we need to ask is: 'How did World War 1 start?'

In this unit, you will learn about the **long-term** and the **short-term** causes of the war. The box below contains keywords or phrases that you will find useful for this topic.

Keyword	Definition
cause	a reason why something happens
long-term cause	something that has been going on for a long time
short-term cause	an event that makes something happen quickly
empire	a group of countries that are owned by one country
alliance	a group of countries that promise to help each other
colony	a country that is ruled by another country
assassination	the murder of a person for political reasons
invade	sending soldiers into another country to take it over
arms race	countries try to get more weapons than each other
industry	factories and mines that give a country its money

World War 1

Why was Europe ready for a war? (1)

At the beginning of 1914, George V was king of Great Britain and its empire. Great Britain was the most powerful country in the world. Germany and many other countries were very envious of Great Britain's power. Germany's ruler in 1914 was Kaiser Wilhelm II.

Below are the **long-term causes** of World War 1:

My country is the most powerful in the world. We have a huge **empire** and lots of **industry**. That means we are very rich. We like being the most powerful country in the world, so we have a strong army and navy to make sure that nobody beats us!

King George V

My country should be the most powerful in the world! We have a large **empire** and lots of **industry**, but we need more to be the best. We need to get more **colonies** and build a bigger army and navy than the British. We also need more weapons – then we will be able show them who is the boss! I know lots of countries that do not like Great Britain. We will all join together in an **alliance** against the British. We will be like a football team and we will all help each other!

Kaiser Wilhelm II

Why was Europe ready for a war? (2)

I have teamed up with **Austro-Hungary**. They have a big empire too! We will help each other and that way we become more powerful. We are going to call our alliance team the **TRIPLE ALLIANCE!**

Germany + Austro-Hungary = The Triple Alliance

I will not let this happen! We will try to get more colonies and we will build more weapons so that we remain the best. We will also form an alliance of our own. Germany has many enemies who are also our friends. We will form a team with **France** and **Russia**. We will call our alliance the **TRIPLE ENTENTE!**

Great Britain + France + Russia = The Triple Entente

Europe was now split into two teams. Both sides had huge empires that were spread all over the world. All the colonies in these empires had to do as their rulers said. Both the Triple Alliance and the Triple Entente did not like or trust each other and tried to irritate each other whenever they could. Both teams were ready for a war.

All they needed was a reason to fight!

Activity sheet – How did World War 1 start?

The long-term causes of the war

☞ Each box below contains a long-term cause of the war. Under each cause, write a sentence explaining why the cause helped to make Europe ready for a war. Use the information in the resource sheets 'Why was Europe ready for a war? (1)' and '(2)' to help you.

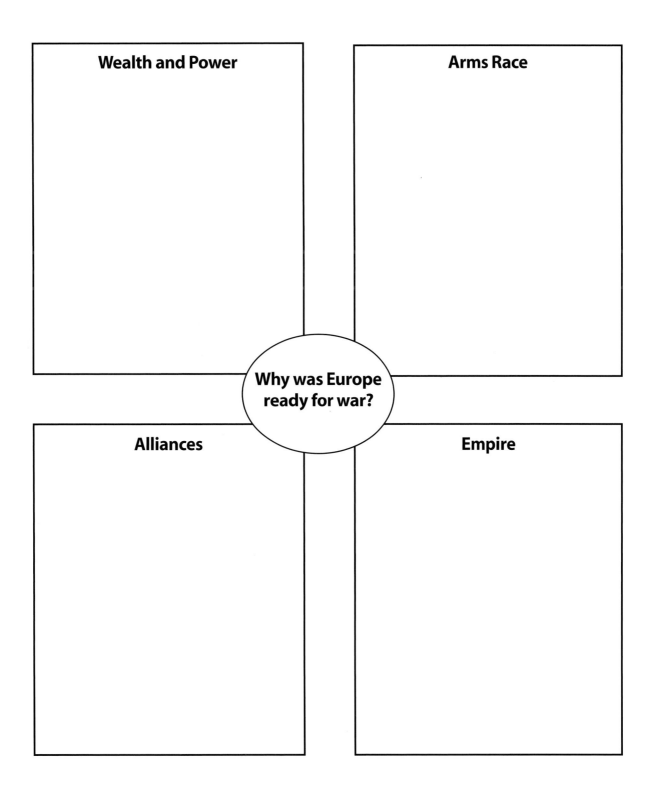

Wealth and Power

Arms Race

Why was Europe ready for war?

Alliances

Empire

Short-term causes: the excuse for war!

Europe was divided into two teams – the **Triple Alliance** and the **Triple Entente.** Both teams were angry at each other and were ready for a war. In the summer of 1914, they got the excuse they needed to start one.

THE TIMES

Archduke Assassinated!

The heir to the throne of Austro-Hungary was murdered today in Sarajevo. The killers were terrorists from Serbia. Serbia is the enemy of **Austro-Hungary.**

Austro-Hungary demands justice and says that Serbia is to blame. **Austro-Hungary** says that if Serbia does not deal with the problem it will declare war on them! What will happen next?

On 28 June 1914, a Serbian terrorist group called the Black Hand assassinated Archduke Franz Ferdinand and his pregnant wife. Franz was next in line for the throne of Austro-Hungary and he was on an official visit to Sarajevo. Austro-Hungary blamed Serbia for the deaths and declared war on them on 28 July 1914.

The other members of the two alliances had to support the countries on their teams. Soon all of Europe was at war.

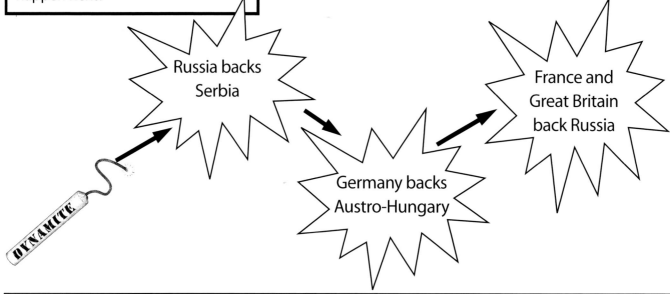

1. Russia backs Serbia
2. Germany backs Austro-Hungary
3. France and Great Britain back Russia

☞ On a separate sheet of paper, write your answers to the questions below.

1 What were the names of the two alliances (teams) in Europe?

2 Who was Archduke Franz Ferdinand?

3 Why was Austro-Hungary angry at Serbia?

4 Why did other countries get involved in the argument between Austro-Hungary and Serbia?

Teacher's notes

Why did men join the army?

Objectives

- Understand that the government needed a lot of men to join the army
- Learn the different reasons why men joined the army
- Use sources effectively

Prior knowledge

Students need to be aware that there had never been a world war before, and all previous conflicts had been relatively short.

QCA link

Unit 18 Twentieth-century conflicts

NC links

History skills 2a, 4b
Breadth of study 13, the two world wars

Scottish attainment targets

Environmental Studies – Society – People in the past
Strand – People, events and societies of significance in the past
Level D
Strand – Change, continuity, cause and effect
Level D

Northern Ireland PoS

Study Unit 4: The twentieth-century world, a) The impact of world war, World War I
Study Units 5 and 6: c) A significant era or turning point in history, the First World War

added the benefits of peer pressure to the recruitment process and it was a boost to morale to know you would be with your friends. The campaign was further aided by the lack of media coverage of warfare and high unemployment at home. Joining up seemed like a good option for many.

Starter activity

Discuss with the students what the term 'war' means to them. Encourage them to explain their answers and try to draw out why they know so much about warfare today.

Resource sheet and activity sheets

Use 'It will all be over by Christmas!' to discuss with the class the message shown in the recruitment poster.

'How did recruitment posters convince men to join up?' provides three more posters for the students to look at independently. It gives students an insight into how the posters pulled at emotions.

'Create your own recruitment poster' encourages students to develop their understanding of the persuasive methods used by the government in 1914 by designing a recruitment poster.

'Why did you join the army?' and 'Character cards' provide an empathy task that encourages students to consider joining up from an individual's perspective. The character cards can be used throughout this book to enhance students' understanding of the topics.

Plenary

Discuss the different reasons that people had for joining up and list them on the board. Then invite the class to vote on which reason they think was the most powerful.

Background

In 1914, the British government believed that the war would be a short, sharp affair. They also believed that their success in the war rested on the size of their army. Therefore it was necessary to recruit large numbers of soldiers very quickly. They used a variety of tactics to encourage recruits, but the most successful was the poster campaign that appealed to all aspects of society. Similarly, the creation of the 'Pals' regiments

It will all be over by Christmas!

Once the war had started, thousands of men volunteered to join the army and fight for their country. Everyone believed that Britain was so strong that it would win. They thought that the war would be over by Christmas 1914. The volunteers wanted the chance to fight for their country. They did not want to miss out.

Recruiting begins

The government believed that England would need an army of millions to beat the Germans by Christmas. They started a massive recruiting campaign to convince more men to join up. Recruiting offices opened in every town and city. Famous people spoke to crowds encouraging them to hate the Germans and fight for their country.

The poster campaign

The government also began a huge poster advertising campaign. These posters were very successful and they made thousands of men join up. Different types of poster were created to appeal to different kinds of people. Each poster was designed to convince a person that joining the army was the right thing to do.

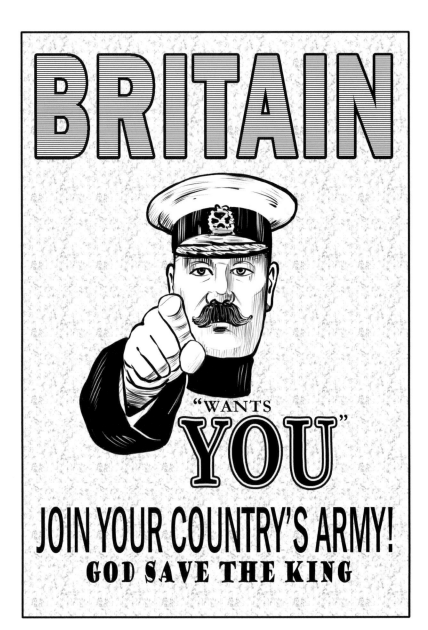

How does this poster try to make an appeal?

World War 1

Activity sheet – Why did men join the army?

How did recruitment posters convince men to join up?

☞ Look closely at the two posters from World War 1. On a separate sheet of paper, write your answers to the questions below each poster.

Daddy, what did YOU do in the Great War?

How is this poster trying to make men feel?

What do you think this poster is saying?

WOMEN OF BRITAIN SAY "GO!"

How is this poster trying to make women feel?

What do you think this poster is saying?

☞ Work with a partner to make a list of the different types of feelings people would have had when they saw these recruitment posters. Do you think they would have convinced people to join up?

Create your own recruitment poster

☞ Imagine it is 1914. You have been asked by the British government to design a poster to convince more men to join the army to fight in the war. Think about:

- which feelings people have that you can use to convince them to join the army
- a good slogan that is easily remembered
- why it is important to fight in the war.

Why did you join the army?

The government created 'Pals' regiments to encourage people to join up. These were regiments made up of people from the same place, so that friends could be together when they fought.

Whole villages, factories or even football teams joined up together and fought together. Many men joined up because all the men they knew were joining up. They felt they had no choice!

Because of all this, the government was able to recruit tens of thousands of soldiers in the early part of the war.

 Imagine you are a young man in 1914. You have just joined the army with all your friends. Choose one of the following character cards and stick it in your book. Give your character a name. You will be using this character again in the future.

On a separate sheet of paper, write a page in your diary explaining why you joined the army. Think about:

- What convinced you to join the army
- How you feel about fighting a war
- How you hope other people will think of you.

You might like to start your diary like this ⟶

1914

Dear diary

I have just gone to the army recruitment office with my friends. We have all joined the army to fight in the war!

I feel _____

I am trying to be brave because _____

_____

I hope that when I return _____

_____

Character cards

The character cards below give you details of different people who joined the army. You should select a card and give the character a name and a personality. These cards will be used throughout the topic and in the 'Over the top!' game towards the end of the book.

You are almost 16 years old and too young to enlist. You lie about your age so that you can join your friends. You are an only child. Your father is already dead and you help your mother to run the family dairy farm.

You are the squire's youngest son. You are 18 years old and are just about to go to university to study medicine. You don't really want to join the army, but feel that you must because your father and brother are also enlisting.

You are a farmer. You are 39 and married with four children. Your eldest son is 19 and he is enlisting with you. Your wife says she can manage the farm with the other boys until you get back. You are looking forward to seeing another country as you have never been abroad.

You are the village doctor. You are 32 years old and have a wife and twin babies. You are the only doctor for 25 miles, so many local communities rely on you for medical help.

You are the local mill owner, and you grind most of the local farmers' wheat into flour so that they can sell it on. You are 36 and have four children. Your eldest is only 17 and he is enlisting with you.

You are the butler in the manor house. You have worked hard to earn the position. You live in accommodation at the house with your wife who is pregnant with your first child. You are 28.

You are a farmer. You are 30 and already a widower. Your wife died in childbirth four years ago. You live with your mother, who helps you take care of your young daughter.

You are the miller's son and you are just 17. Your father signed your enlistment papers so that you could both go together. You are proud to be fighting for your country and you hope to take over the mill when your father retires.

You are a carpenter and you work hard around the village doing repairs and making things for the villagers and the squire. You are 26 and will be marrying your sweetheart as soon as you get back.

You are the local squire. You own a big manor house and employ many people from the village on your land. You are 40, married and have two grown up sons who have both joined up with you.

You are the teacher at the village school. You teach all 20 of the local children. You are married and have three children. Your children are under the age of four so you do not teach them yet … but you are looking forward to that. You are 30 years old.

You are the local baker with a small shop in the village. You are 28 years old. You took over the business from you father, who is too ill to work any more. You support him and your mother as well as your wife and three children.

World War 1

Teacher's notes

What were the trenches like?

Objectives

- Identify the different parts of a trench
- Understand why trenches were used on the Western Front
- Discover what conditions were like in the trenches

Prior knowledge

Students need to be aware that the landscape along the Western Front was very flat and offered little protection for soldiers.

QCA link

Unit 18 Twentieth-century conflicts

NC links

History skills 4a, 4b
Breadth of study 13, the two world wars

Scottish attainment targets

Environmental Studies – Society – People in the past
Strand – Change and continuity, cause and effect
Level E

Northern Ireland PoS

Study Unit 4: The twentieth-century world, a) The impact of world war, World War I
Study Units 5 and 6: c) A significant era or turning point in history, the First World War

Starter activities

Using the keywords from the units so far, ask various students to give a definition for the different words or phrases.

Resource sheets and activity sheets

'Inside a World War 1 trench' provides a cross-section of a trench. Ask the students to look closely at the picture to see if they can work out what the different parts of the trench are for. This could lead into a discussion about whether or not fighting in a trench is a good or bad idea.

'Understanding the trenches' is a follow-on activity that invites the students to define what each part of a trench was for.

'The war was not the only problem!' is a follow-on activity where students can expand their knowledge of trench life by matching a trench problem to a solution.

'The terrible trenches' gives students the opportunity to consolidate all their learning from the unit by creating a mind map. This activity could involve the students adding lots of information and detail to the mind map where they explain a particular issue and provide the solutions, or it could be used as a quick discussion plenary task.

Plenary

Ask the students to recap the main trench problems briefly, such as lice, mud, rats and so on and write these words on the board. Invite the students to write a sentence that summarises trench conditions that must use all of the words on the board, and must make sense. Give rewards for the fastest student and the best sentence.

Background

At the beginning of World War 1, nobody foresaw a war that would last for years. Trenches were dug out of necessity and not because they were considered the best way to fight. The landscape along the Western Front did not provide many natural boundaries between the two opposing armies, so they had to make their own. Unfortunately, by taking the war into the trenches, the two alliances created a situation that was very difficult to end and created a stalemate that would not be broken for at least three years. The temporary trenches soon developed into a complex and organised trench system that stretched for hundreds of miles.

Resource sheet – What were the trenches like?

Inside a World War 1 trench

☞ Below is a cross-section of a front line trench. In pairs, look closely at the picture and try to work out what the different parts of the trench were for.

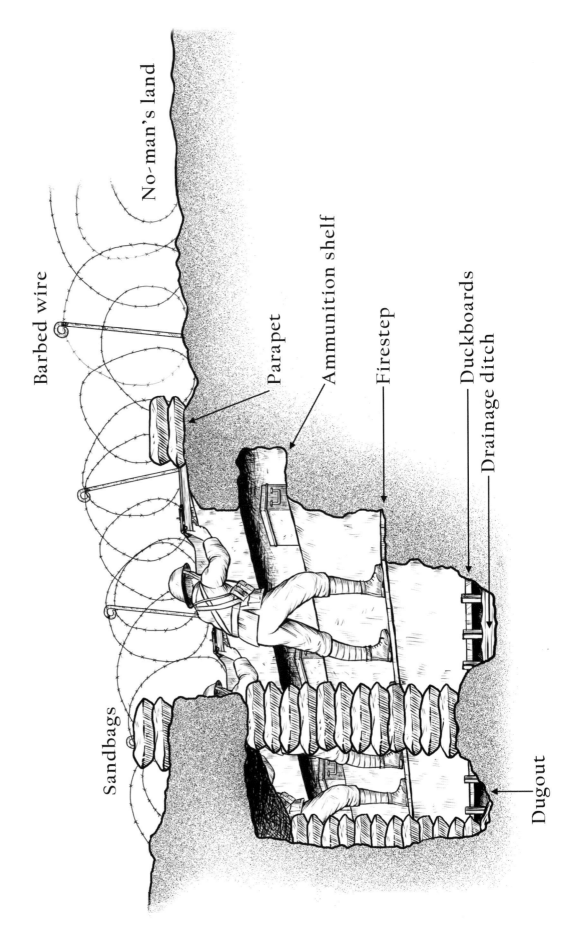

No-man's land

Barbed wire

Parapet

Ammunition shelf

Firestep

Duckboards

Drainage ditch

Sandbags

Dugout

World War 1

Understanding the trenches

When the war broke out, everybody believed it would be over quickly. They were wrong! Both sides were strong and nobody was winning. This is called a **stalemate**. As the winter started on the **Western Front**, the two sides had no choice but to stay put. The land was very flat and there was nowhere to hide from the enemy, so both sides dug trenches to fight in. These trenches stretched for many miles. The **stalemate** lasted for nearly four years.

 Complete the sentences below by using the keywords from the word bank to fill in the blanks. Use the resource sheet 'Inside a World War 1 trench' to help you.

> **Word bank**
>
> No-man's land   sandbags   dugouts   firestep   Western
>
> duckboards   ammunition   barbed wire   ditch

On the _____ Front, the two armies fought in trenches. A trench was about two and a half metres deep. The area between the two enemies' trenches was named _____. It was a very dangerous place. It was covered in _____, which is very sharp and would tear your skin. This made it very difficult to cross. The main part of the trench would be protected with _____. The floor of the trench was covered in _____ to keep the bottom dry. The rainwater was collected in a drainage _____ underneath. To be able to fire your gun at the enemy, you had to stand on a _____. Spare bullets would be kept on the _____ shelf. In the sides of the trenches were _____. This is where the soldiers had shelter or slept.

The war was not the only problem!

 The following cards show a selection of problems that soldiers faced in the trenches and also the solutions they came up with to solve these problems. Cut out all the cards and match each problem to the correct solution.

SOLUTION

Soldiers had to shave often and make sure that their hair was very short. They would also check each other for eggs and try to get rid of them. In very bad cases, the uniforms would be burned.

PROBLEM

Trench foot
The wet and muddy conditions in the trenches caused feet to swell up and go black. The flesh would go rotten and the soldiers would be in terrible pain.

SOLUTION

The soldiers dug small pits next to the main trenches. These pits were covered with planks of wood for the soldiers to sit on. When they were full, they were covered in mud. They were called latrines and were smelly.

PROBLEM

Lice
The trenches did not have running water or showers, so soldiers found it very hard to keep clean. They soon became infected with lice that lived on all parts of their bodies.

SOLUTION

The soldiers would rub waterproof oil, such as whale oil, on their feet. They also had to change their socks regularly. In bad cases the toes, or the whole foot, would have to be cut off.

PROBLEM

Rats
The dirty conditions and the lack of storage attracted rats to the trenches. The rats ate the soldiers' rations and crawled all over them when they slept. They carried diseases.

SOLUTION

Soldiers had to protect rations by putting them in boxes or by tying them in bundles and hanging them from the roof of the dugouts. Sometimes soldiers would shoot at them.

PROBLEM

Toilets
There was no running water or sewage pipes in the trenches. This meant that proper toilets could not be fitted.

World War 1

The terrible trenches

☞ **Class discussion point:**

Why were trenches such dangerous places?

☞ Use your knowledge of trenches to complete the diagram below.

What were the trenches like during World War 1?

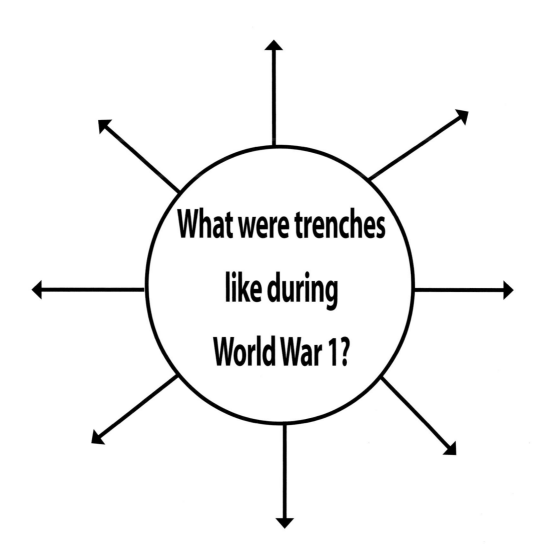

Teacher's notes

What weapons were used in the war?

Objectives

- Understand that warfare had changed a great deal in 50 years
- Understand that new technology had led to different weapons
- Learn the different types of gas that were used and their effects

Prior knowledge

Students need to know that there had never been a modern war before and that previous wars had involved more hand-to-hand combat.

QCA link

Unit 18 Twentieth-century conflicts

NC links

History skills 4b, 5c, 7a
Breadth of study 13, the two world wars

Scottish attainment targets

Environmental Studies – Society – People in the past
Strand – People, events and societies of significance in the past
Level D
Strand – Change, continuity, cause and effect
Level D

Northern Ireland PoS

Study Unit 4: The twentieth-century world, a) The impact of world war, World War I
Study Units 5 and 6: c) A significant era or turning point in history, the First World War

Background

World War 1 is considered to be the first 'technological' war. This is because weapons and technology had evolved that made killing the enemy less personal and more efficient. The speed of machine guns, the strength of tanks and the spying capabilities of aircraft meant that armies had to be ready for anything at any time. In reality, these new weapons were in their infancy and were often not very effective. Gas, for example, was unpredictable and did not kill as many as it was intended to. Aeroplanes had little effective battle use, and the first tanks were slow and did more to increase morale than actually make a significant impact on the war. However, the machine gun proved itself to be a very deadly weapon.

Starter activity

Ask students to write down a weapon that is used in war today and one that was used in a war from the past that they have studied (such as the Battle of Hastings). Ask them to compare the two weapons and to decide which one would be better at killing people and why. The aim is to encourage the students to think about how warfare has changed and why these changes happened.

Resource sheets and activity sheets

In pairs or groups, invite the students to study the pictures in 'Two battlefields' and to identify the main areas of change in both weapons and tactics. Ask each pair or group to give feedback to the class. This could be followed by a discussion on the information that the students have discovered on how different World War 1 had been from all previous conflicts.

'How had fighting a war changed?' helps students to consolidate their learning by comparing the effectiveness of the weapons and tactics used in the pictures on the 'Two battlefields' resource sheet.

'Toxic!' gives students a brief summary of the three main gases used as weapons in the war and how they could be overcome.

In 'Gas attack!', students should present the information from 'Toxic!' in their own way. This activity could be extended by inviting students to carry out some private research on gas attacks in World War 1, so that their finished leaflet is more detailed and their own knowledge expanded.

Plenary

Undertake a quick quiz in which the students are given the result, or effect, of one of the weapons from World War 1. They should then try to correctly identify the weapon used.

Resource sheet – What weapons were used in the war?

Two battlefields

These two pictures show how fighting a war has changed over time.

Great Britain fights a battle in the Crimean War, 1854

Great Britain fights a battle in World War 1, 1917

How had fighting a war changed?

☞ Complete the table below by making a list of the weapons and tactics that the British army used in the Crimean War and World War 1. Use the pictures on resource sheet 'Two battlefields' to help you.

The Crimean War, 1854	World War 1, 1917

☞ Use the information from your table to answer these questions:

1. Which war do you think it would have been more dangerous to fight in, World War 1 or the Crimean War?

   _____

2. Why did you make this choice?

   _____

   _____

3. What new weapons were used during World War 1?

   _____

   _____

4. Which of these new weapons do you believe was the most dangerous and why?

   _____

   _____

Toxic!

The German army also had a new kind of weapon. They used poison gas to kill or injure the enemy. This was a very difficult weapon to control because it was carried by wind. If the wind blew the wrong way, the gas would attack the German troops instead of their enemy! They used three different kinds of gas:

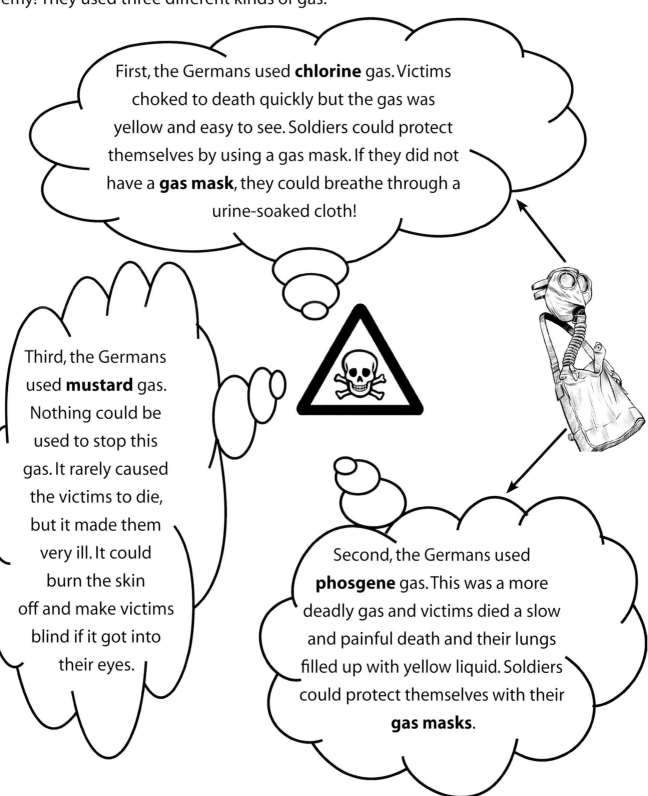

First, the Germans used **chlorine** gas. Victims choked to death quickly but the gas was yellow and easy to see. Soldiers could protect themselves by using a gas mask. If they did not have a **gas mask**, they could breathe through a urine-soaked cloth!

Third, the Germans used **mustard** gas. Nothing could be used to stop this gas. It rarely caused the victims to die, but it made them very ill. It could burn the skin off and make victims blind if it got into their eyes.

Second, the Germans used **phosgene** gas. This was a more deadly gas and victims died a slow and painful death and their lungs filled up with yellow liquid. Soldiers could protect themselves with their **gas masks**.

Gas attack!

Use the frame below to create a leaflet about gas for soldiers fighting in the trenches during World War 1. Your leaflet must warn soldiers about the dangers of the different types of gas and it must give them information on how they should protect themselves. Use the information from the resource sheet 'Toxic!' to help you.

How to survive a gas attack!

Teacher's notes

Why did so many die at the Somme?

Objectives

- Understand that thousands died at the Somme
- Learn the different reasons why Field Marshall Haig's plan failed
- Empathise with the soldiers in the battle
- Communicate knowledge in a letter

Prior knowledge

Students need to know that the stalemate on the Western Front had been going on for two years.

QCA links

Unit 18 Twentieth-century conflicts

NC links

History skills 2c, 2e, 5c
Breadth of study 13, the two world wars

Scottish attainment targets

Environmental Studies – Society – People in the past
Strand – Change and continuity, cause and effect
Level E
Strand – People, events and societies of significance in the past
Level E

Northern Ireland PoS

Study Unit 4: The twentieth-century world, a) The impact of world war, World War I *The Battle of the Somme 1916*
Study Units 5 and 6: c) A significant era or turning point in history, the First World War

Background

Field Marshall Haig took command of the British army at the turn of 1916. At the same time, the ranks of the army increased dramatically because of conscription. Haig wanted to capitalise on this and planned the Somme offensive with General Joffre, the French Commander-in-Chief. He hoped these tactics would gain them an advantage in the war and help to break the stalemate. Haig was a single-minded individual who refused to see the flaws in his battle plan, and would not change tactics even when the French were unable to assist at the Somme. The resulting battle raged for five months, and Haig's objectives were never met. The loss of life on both sides was enormous. The first day of the battle was the bloodiest in British military history, with over 60 000 casualties.

Starter activity

Explain what the term 'over the top' meant. Remind students that the trenches were meant to protect the soldiers from danger. Put the following sentence on the board and ask the students to finish it using at least ten words: 'The Captain ordered us to go over the top into No-man's land, I felt…'.

Resource sheets and activity sheet

Use 'The Battle of the Somme' to explain Haig's plan and objectives and to encourage students to consider what problems could occur.

'Lions led by donkeys!' provides further information about the battle.

Encourage students to discuss the different problems that the British encountered and ask them what they would do differently and what Haig did wrong.

'15 things to know about the Somme' provides questions about the battle and gives students an opportunity to select relevant information about the battle to help them to understand why it went wrong.

'A letter from the trenches' asks the students to produce a written answer independently. Using the 'character' they were given from the resource sheet 'Character cards', they should write a letter home about their experiences on the first day of the Somme. The finished letter can be photocopied to use in the next unit 'How did the government hide the truth?' as it can be censored.

The continuity of using the same 'character' in this and future units gives students a personal and emotional link to the topic.

'Keyword collection' gives students the opportunity to ensure that they understand the meanings of some of the keywords they have learned in units 1–5. This activity could also be used as a starter or plenary activity for some of the later units.

Plenary

Students could read their letters aloud and then take a vote on the most interesting letter.

The Battle of the Somme

By 1916, everybody was tired of fighting in the trenches. The **stalemate** was not broken and the situation was much the same as it had been in the winter of 1914. The new Commander-in-Chief of the British army, Field Marshall Sir Douglas Haig, believed that something had to be done to break the stalemate. The British army had just got bigger because thousands of volunteers had joined up and Haig decided that this would help win the war for Britain and her allies.

The stalemate has gone on long enough. We will use all our new recruits and join forces with the French. Together we will attack the German trenches near the River Somme. Such a large attack will allow us to push the German army back, and maybe they will **retreat** or **surrender**! Most people do not believe my plan will work, but I know that it will. This will be the battle that ends the war!

Field Marshall Sir Douglas Haig

The plan

1 British and French artillery would destroy the German barbed wire and trenches.

2 Aeroplanes would check that the German defences had been destroyed.

3 Soldiers and tanks would easily pass the cut barbed wire on No-man's land.

4 The British and French soldiers would capture the German trenches and break the stalemate.

Lions led by donkeys!

On the morning of 1 July 1916, the British and French soldiers went over the top to begin the Battle of the Somme. Within an hour, over 30 000 of these soldiers had been wounded and many died later. By the end of the first day, the total number of wounded soldiers increased to 60 000! The attack had been a complete disaster and the Battle of the Somme went on for another five months and killed over one million British, French and German soldiers. It was the biggest failure in British military history. But why did it fail?

What really happened

1 The French were stuck at another battle in Verdun, so the British had very little French help.

2 The Germans saw the British preparing a path and cutting their barbed wire weeks before the attack.

3 Most of the artillery shells fired at the German defences did not explode because they were faulty.

4 The German soldiers hid in huge underground shelters, so the artillery did not kill them.

5 The artillery had failed to cut through the barbed wire near the German trenches.

6 The new British soldiers did not know how to fight and got stuck on the barbed wire.

7 Most of the new tanks broke down and could not be used in the battle.

8 The sky was too cloudy, so the planes could not see if the German defences had been destroyed.

9 The German soldiers left the shelters and used machine guns to kill the British trapped on the barbed wire in No-man's land. Over 21 000 British died on the first day of the Battle of the Somme. Haig would not change tactics so the killing carried on for months and in the end the British had taken only a few miles of enemy trenches.

15 things to know about the Somme

☞ On a separate sheet of paper, write the answers to the following questions. Use the resource sheets 'The Battle of the Somme' and 'Lions led by donkeys!' to help you.

7 How did the Germans know that the British were planning to attack?	**6** Why could the French not help the British?	**5** What was used to try to cut the German barbed wire?	**4** What did Haig believe the battle would achieve?
8 What was wrong with the British artillery?			**3** Why had the British army just got bigger?
9 How did the Germans keep safe from the British artillery?	**START HERE** ⟹	**1** When did the Battle of the Somme start?	**2** Who was the Commander-in-Chief of the British army?
10 Why were the British soldiers not good at fighting?			
11 Why were the British army not helped by their tanks?	*The Battle of the Somme*		
12 Why did the planes not see that the enemy guns were still there?	**13** Why was the German barbed wire a problem?	**14** How many British soldiers were killed on the first day?	**15** How long did the Battle of the Somme last?

World War 1

A letter from the trenches

☞ You are a soldier at the Battle of the Somme. It is the end of the first day of the battle. You have survived but most of your friends have not. In the frame below, write a letter home telling your family about what happened. Use your knowledge of the trenches and the Battle of the Somme, your character card and the checklist below to help you.

What did you see? ☐   How many died? ☐   How do you feel? ☐

How did you survive? ☐   What went wrong? ☐   What will happen next? ☐

1 July 1916
The Somme
France

Dear _____

Today was the worst day of my life. I am lucky to be alive. This is because _____

_____

_____

_____

_____

_____

_____

_____

_____

Lots of love

_____

Activity sheet – Why did so many die at the Somme?

Keyword collections

☞ Draw a line to match each keyword to the correct definition.

Keyword	Definition
Gas mask	A yellow gas that made soldiers choke to death if they were not wearing their gas masks.
Trench foot	A situation where both sides cannot move forward to win.
No-man's land	Soldiers would wear this to help them to breathe when poisons were in the air.
Triple Alliance	The name given to the space between two enemy trenches.
Chlorine gas	An infection caused by wearing wet shoes and socks that often led to amputation.
Assassination	A deadly gas that could cause blindness or serious burns on the skin.
Barbed wire	The name given to the alliance between Germany, Austro-Hungary and Italy.
Stalemate	The name given to the alliance between Great Britain, France and Russia.
Mustard gas	When men were ordered to leave the trenches to fight the enemy.
Triple Entente	The murder of someone for political reasons.
Western Front	Sharp metal coils that could rip the skin off soldiers and stopped them from getting past.
Over the top	The name given to the battlegrounds that went through France and Belgium.

Teacher's notes

How did the government hide the truth?

Objectives

- Understand what censorship is
- Understand why the government censored the news
- Discover how the government censored letters

Prior knowledge

Students need to know that the world was not as technologically advanced during World War 1 as it is today. They also need to have completed the unit 'Why did so many die at the Somme?'.

QCA links

Unit 18 Twentieth-century conflicts

NC links

History skills 2a, 3a, 3b
Breadth of study 13, the two world wars

Scottish attainment targets

Environmental Studies – Society – People in the past
Strand – People, events and societies of significance in the past
Level D
Strand – Change and continuity, cause and effect
Level E

Northern Ireland PoS

Study Unit 4: The twentieth-century world, a) The impact of world war, World War I
Study Units 5 and 6: c) A significant era or turning point in history, the First World War

Background

Censorship was widely used by the British government during wartime, and this continued well into the twentieth century. It was also remarkably successful because of the lack of technology available. News was slow to travel, and people relied on newspapers or the silent newsreels shown at cinemas to keep them informed.

Censorship and propaganda ensured that the general public were behind the government and supported the war effort. It also ensured a steady supply of new volunteers into the armed services.

Photographic images were strictly controlled during World War 1, and this meant that the true horror of the war was not widely understood until after 1918.

Starter activity

Place the following anagrams on the board for students to solve: mosem (Somme), chernt (trench), kamssag (gas mask). Award a prize for the first student to get all three words correct.

Resource sheets and activity sheets

Ask the students to read 'The News'. Discuss with them the headlines from the British newspapers after the first day of the Battle of the Somme. Do they match up to what they know about the Somme offensive?

Follow this with 'Hot off the press!' This shows students that the press were often economical with the truth, or focused on the positives and ignored the negatives.

'The whole truth and nothing but the truth' provides a template for students to write an uncensored account of the first day at the Somme. These can then be compared to the 'official' version in a discussion about why the government censored the news and how they did it.

'Censor cards' provides useful guidelines for students to help them censor text.

'Censored!' gives students the opportunity to think like a censor during World War 1. They can practise their skills on the letter provided, and then censor the letters they wrote on resource sheet 'A letter from the trenches'. By censoring each other's work using the 'Censor cards' resource sheet, the students can see how frustrating it must have been to those at home to receive a letter that told them nothing, or was incomplete.

Plenary

Read a story from one of today's newspapers to the class. Ask for a few volunteers to retell the story to the class as if it has been censored in the same way as the news reports from World War 1.

The news

Today we are surrounded by news – on the radio, television, Internet and in newspapers. People today are very well informed and we take it for granted that if something important happens, we will be told about it straight away. We also expect to be told the truth. This was not always the case.

During World War 1, the government felt it was necessary to hide the truth from the public. In this way, they could convince people that the war was a good idea and that it was going well. To do this, they selected the information that they gave to the public and hid what they did not want the public to see. This is called **censorship.**

There was no television or Internet during World War 1 because it had not been invented. Radio was also very new and it had not started to broadcast the news. The only way people could find out what was happening was to read newspapers or go to see newsreels at the cinema.

In many ways, the Somme was a disaster for the British. However, it was not reported that way in 1916! The government **censored** the newspaper reports so that the public believed that everything at the Somme was going to plan, as these headlines from the time show:

The glorious 1st of July

British soldiers eager for the battle

Heaps of German dead

Great success at the Somme

OVER 7500 PRISONERS CAPTURED

Hot off the press!

The following newspaper report is based on the type of front pages that were seen in Britain after the first day of the Battle of the Somme. As you can see, the newspapers were showing a very different version of events from those that you have been studying. This is because the British government **censored** the news. This means that they stopped the newspapers from printing information that may have upset the public or made people think that the war was not going well.

THE DAILY NEWS

LONDON, SUNDAY 2ND JULY 1916　　　ONE HALFPENNY

GREAT SUCCESS OF BRITISH ATTACK ON THE SOMME

Yesterday the British and French army bravely attacked the German trenches at the Somme. This attack had been carefully planned months in advance and the troops had been rehearsing for the battle for several weeks, so that no mistakes would be made.

Before the troops went over the top, the enemy trenches had been bombarded with artillery fire. This meant that most of the German soldiers were already dead before the battle started.

With the help of tanks and bombs, our brave boys were able to take the enemy trenches easily, passing thousands of dead German soldiers on their way.

There were, of course, British casualties, but our losses were slight compared to those of the enemy. Those Germans left alive were happy to be taken prisoner.

By the end of the day, our heroes had managed to take several miles of enemy trenches. Field Marshall Haig called the day 'a great success'.

The whole truth and nothing but the truth

Complete the template below by writing your own newspaper front page that tells the truth about the Battle of the Somme. Use the resource sheet 'Lions led by donkeys!' to help you.

THE DAILY NEWS

LONDON, SUNDAY 2ND JULY 1916   ONE HALFPENNY

Resource sheet – How did the government hide the truth?

Censor cards

Use these cards to help with the activity sheet 'Censored!'

Cross out any words or sentences that say <u>WHERE</u> the soldiers are fighting.	Cross out any words or sentences that say <u>THAT BRITISH SOLDIERS HAVE DIED.</u>
Cross out any words or sentences that say <u>THAT THE BRITISH SOLDIERS ARE SCARED.</u>	Cross out any words or sentences that say <u>THE TRENCHES ARE DANGEROUS OR DIRTY.</u>
Cross out any words or sentences that say <u>THE ARMY LEADERS HAVE MADE MISTAKES OR ARE STUPID.</u>	Cross out any words or sentences that say <u>WHAT THE SOLDIERS ARE GOING TO DO NEXT OR WHERE THEY ARE GOING.</u>
Cross out any words or sentences that say <u>THE WAR IS NOT A GOOD IDEA.</u>	Cross out any words or sentences that say <u>THE GERMANS ARE WINNING OR THE BRITISH ARE LOSING.</u>

Censored!

To make sure that the public did not find out the truth from any family or friends who were fighting in the trenches, letters were also **censored**. The **army censor** would read all the letters before they were sent. Any information that was thought to be unsuitable was crossed out using a thick black pen, or parts of the paper were actually cut out of the letter. This stopped people reading things that the government thought that they should not see.

☞ Use the letter below and cross out any parts that the government would have censored. Use the resource sheet 'Censor cards' to help you.

> Saturday 1st July, 1916
> The Somme
> France
>
> Dear Mum,
>
> Today was the worst day of my life. I have never been so scared, but I know that I am one of the lucky ones because I am still alive. So many men died today! We went over the top at dawn. We have been practising for this battle for weeks, but nothing went the way it was supposed to. The generals said that our artillery were supposed to kill all the Germans and cut through the barbed wire so that we could attack. They lied to us! The barbed wire was still there and thousands of men got trapped in it. The Germans were also still alive and they all seemed to have machine guns. In front of me, all I could see was a sea of dead bodies. All our men, some of them only boys, were hanging on the barbed wire. The ground was red with blood. All you could hear was bullets and the screaming of the men who were not quite dead. We could not save them and we could not turn back. The officers just kept sending the men over the top. Why didn't they stop? I was lucky, even though most of my friends are dead, I managed to get back to the trench alive. I have never been so happy to see this disgusting hole in the ground! I want to come home Mum, this war is pointless and we cannot win.
>
> I hope I see you again.
>
> John

Teacher's notes

How did soldiers feel about the war?

Objectives

- Understand that many soldiers did not support the war
- Be able to extract information from sources
- Be familiar with and use some historical keywords

Prior knowledge

Students need to know that many soldiers were conscripted into the army by the government. Although there were many volunteers, the majority of the British army by 1916 was made up of conscripts.

QCA links

Unit 18 Twentieth-century conflicts

NC links

History skills 3a, 3b, 7b
Breadth of study 13, the two world wars

Scottish attainment targets

Environmental Studies – Society – People in the past
Strand – Change and continuity, cause and effect
Level E
Strand – The nature of historical evidence
Level D

Northern Ireland POS

Study Unit 4: The twentieth-century world, a) The impact of world war, World War I
Study Units 5 and 6: c) A significant era or turning point in history, the First World War

Background

By the end of 1916, after the terrible events of the Battle of the Somme and Passchendale, many people became critical of the war. For many, it had gone on too long, and there was no end in sight, nor a clear objective to fight towards. The British and German governments did their best to hide this from the public, and both used censorship and propaganda to encourage public support for the war. However, there were undercurrents of dissent, especially in the trenches, where mutinies and desertions were becoming more common. This was well hidden at home, but many soldiers knew that if they did not carry on fighting, the punishment was often death.

Starter activity

Write the following question on the board: 'How do we find out about the news today?' Ask for volunteers to each write one different news medium on the board. Continue until students have exhausted all of the possible ways in which the news is conveyed to us.

Resource sheets and activity sheets

Read 'Harry's story (1)' and '(2)' with the class. Explain the keywords as they arise and discuss Harry's experiences as a class.

'What has Harry told us?' provides several questions for students to answer. The discussions arising from Harry's story can be used to help the students to answer these questions. Obviously, there are many more witness accounts to compare Harry's story to, and students could follow up this activity with an Internet search to see if other soldiers shared Harry's views.

'A picture speaks a thousand words' and *'Paths of Glory'* show students how paintings can give an insight into what soldiers felt about the war. It also gives students another opportunity to explore how the government tried to direct public opinion by censorship and propaganda. Again, this activity can be used in comparison to other war paintings. Nevinson painted other contentious pictures, such as *The Harvest of the Battle*. The work of the German artist Otto Dix provides an interesting slant from the other side, and was equally unpopular with the German government at the same time as Nevinson upset the British government.

Plenary

Give each student a sticky note and ask each of them to give a reason why many soldiers had a negative attitude towards the war. Group all of the notes together on the board according to type and see which reason they gave, if any, was the most common.

Harry's story (1)

Harry Patch was only 16 when the war started. His older brother went to fight straight away. He had warned Harry how bad the trenches were. In 1916, when Harry was 18 years old, he was **conscripted** into the army. He did not want to go, but he did not have a choice. After a few months of training, Harry was sent to fight in Belgium. Harry hated the trenches. They were cold and wet and the officers were very strict. Often there was not enough food to eat, but Harry made good friends, and they shared each other's **rations**.

Harry said that the rats in the trenches were as big as cats and they would chew on your boots if you stood still for too long! Lice were another problem because they made you itch. Harry could not get rid of his lice because he had nowhere to wash his clothes or to have a bath.

On his 19th birthday, Harry watched a terrible battle from the trenches. It was the Battle of Passchendale. He saw thousands of soldiers go **over the top** and then get hit by a barrage of **machine gun fire** before they all died. He had never seen anything so horrible. Harry knew that it would be his turn soon.

A few weeks later, Harry's turn came. He waited in the trenches with his friends for the order to go over the top. They were all terrified. When the orders came, they crawled across **No-man's land** because they knew machine gun fire would hit them if they stood up.

Harry's story (2)

Everywhere Harry looked, there were wounded or dead soldiers. Some were English and some were German. Many were screaming in pain, but Harry could not stop to help them.

He came across a British soldier who had been hit by a large piece of **shrapnel**. His chest had been torn apart, and there was a long open wound from his shoulder to his waist. His stomach had been ripped out and was lying next to him on the ground in a deep pool of blood. Harry knew the man was going to die because his injuries were so bad.

Harry went to move away, but the man stopped him. He looked at Harry and begged, 'Shoot me!' Harry knew the man was in great pain so he unclipped his gun but before he could shoot him, the soldier died suddenly. His last word was 'Mother'.

Harry moved on until a German soldier charged towards him with his **bayonet**. Harry knew the man was going to try to kill him, but Harry never fired to kill, and never killed a single enemy soldier during his time in the war. Instead, he shot the man in the shoulder so that the wound would not kill him. A short while later, Harry and his friends were hit by **shrapnel**. Harry was seriously wounded and was sent home to England. His three friends were killed.

Harry never forgot how bad the war had been. He did not talk about it to anyone until his one-hundredth birthday. Harry did not believe World War 1 achieved anything. He believed that no government has the right to send innocent young men to die for their country. He did not want any young man to live through what he did.

Activity sheet – How did soldiers feel about the war?

What has Harry told us?

☞ Use the information in Harry's story to answer the following questions.

Why did Harry not want to go to war?

_____
_____
_____
_____
_____

How does Harry describe the living conditions in the trenches?

_____
_____
_____
_____
_____

What did Harry see at Passchendale?

_____
_____
_____
_____

What does Harry think about war, and why does he think this?

_____
_____
_____
_____
_____
_____
_____
_____
_____
_____
_____
_____
_____
_____

Why do you think Harry was prepared to kill a wounded British soldier but not an enemy soldier?

_____
_____
_____
_____
_____

A picture speaks a thousand words

This picture is based on a painting called *Paths of Glory*. *Paths of Glory* was painted during World War 1 by an artist called Christopher Nevinson. He was not a soldier. When the war broke out, he refused to join the army because he was a **pacifist**. This means he did not agree with violence or killing as a way of solving things. Instead, Christopher joined the Red Cross and drove wounded soldiers to hospital on the **Western Front**. His job was very dangerous and he saw many terrible things. Christopher was asked by the British government to be an **official war artist**. This meant that they could buy any pictures that they liked and publish them back in Great Britain to show the public what was going on in the war. The government used paintings as **propaganda** and they made sure that the images that were shown gave a positive image of the war. *Paths of Glory* was never used by the British government because it did not gave a positive image of the war.

Paths of Glory

 Use this sheet to help you look more closely at the picture in resource sheet 'A picture speaks a thousand words'. Write your answers to the questions in the space provided in each box.

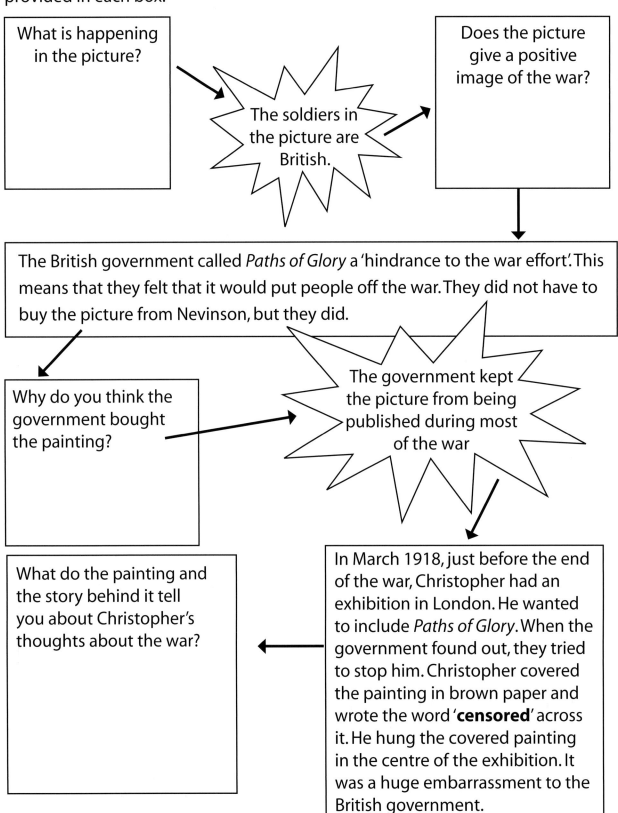

What is happening in the picture?

The soldiers in the picture are British.

Does the picture give a positive image of the war?

The British government called *Paths of Glory* a 'hindrance to the war effort'. This means that they felt that it would put people off the war. They did not have to buy the picture from Nevinson, but they did.

Why do you think the government bought the painting?

The government kept the picture from being published during most of the war

What do the painting and the story behind it tell you about Christopher's thoughts about the war?

In March 1918, just before the end of the war, Christopher had an exhibition in London. He wanted to include *Paths of Glory*. When the government found out, they tried to stop him. Christopher covered the painting in brown paper and wrote the word '**censored**' across it. He hung the covered painting in the centre of the exhibition. It was a huge embarrassment to the British government.

Teacher's notes

How did the war affect people at home?

Objectives

- Understand what the Home Front was
- Be aware of the ways in which women helped in the war effort
- Identify ways in which the government encouraged women to help the Home Front

Prior knowledge

Students need to know that British society was very different before 1914 than it is now, and that men and women had clearly defined roles.

QCA links

Unit 18 Twentieth-century conflicts

NC links

History skills 2a, 3a, 3b
Breadth of study 13, the two world wars

Scottish attainment targets

Environmental Studies – Society – People in the past
Strand – Change and continuity, cause and effect
Level E

Northern Ireland PoS

Study Unit 4: The twentieth-century world, a) The impact of world war, World War I
Study Units 5 and 6: c) A significant era or turning point in history, the First World War

Background

With many men fighting abroad during the war, it became increasingly necessary for women to fill the employment void left. This was a big social change as a woman's place was traditionally seen in the home.

As the war dragged on, it became necessary to increase the production of weapons and equipment to keep the troops at the Front well supplied. The government used propaganda to encourage women to do their bit to help the brave boys save the nation. This included persuading women to leave domestic service and undertake dangerous work in munitions factories. As an incentive, women were briefly paid salaries that competed with those of men. However, this new found 'equality' was short lived as women were expected to step aside when the brave boys came home.

Starter activity

Ask the students to make a list of jobs that they feel women are not capable of. This should produce enough controversy to engage in a short debate about a woman's place in society.

Resource sheet and activity sheets

Use 'The Home Front' to encourage the students to consider what the poster is saying. Who has created the poster? Why have they created it? Is the poster propaganda?

Read and discuss 'The work of women'. Invite students to compare the situation in 1914 with today. 'The war needs women!' asks the students to create a propaganda cartoon that encourages women to work for the war effort. This activity can be extended to allow the students to create an alternative cartoon strip, set in 1914, that states the case for a woman's place staying in the home.

Plenary

Using the alphabet, and starting with the letter A, ask students to think of a keyword from the whole topic that begins with each letter of the alphabet. For example, A = Alliance, B = Barbed wire and so on. Award a prize to the student who gets the most words.

The Home Front

☞ What is this poster trying to say?

World War 1

The work of women

As more and more young men went to fight in the war, it became difficult to find enough people to do the jobs back home. Before the war broke out, Great Britain was a very different place to what it is today. There was a strict **class system** and most women stayed at home to look after their families. There were very few jobs for women. Usually, only unmarried women worked. They often went into **domestic service**. This meant that they worked as maids or servants to the **middle class**.

The wages were very poor, so it was quite easy for the government to convince young women to leave domestic service by paying them more money to work in **munitions factories**.

In these factories, the women made the guns and **shells** that were needed to fight the war. The work was very hard and dangerous. Many women became ill or died because they were breathing in the poisonous chemicals that were used in the **shells**.

Soon women were working in many jobs that had normally been done by men. They worked as bus drivers, miners, chimney sweeps and mechanics, as well as working in all sorts of factories. However, even though they were doing a good job, many people thought that women should not do men's jobs.

Dear Sir

I must protest about the appointment of women van drivers. I feel that they will be a danger to themselves and others. Experienced drivers should do this work, even if they do not come as cheap!

The war needs women!

☞ You have been asked by the government to create a comic strip for a newspaper that must convince women to work in a munitions factory. Complete the template below by drawing a suitable cartoon in each box.

Are you bored of cleaning somebody else's house?	Do you feel guilty that you are safe while our men fight abroad?
Do you dream of a safe future for your children?	Do you feel guilty that you are serving the rich instead of your country?

Work in munitions

With your help, we can win this war!

Teacher's notes

What were your chances of surviving?

Objectives

- Understand that many soldiers died during World War 1
- Appreciate how likely it would be for a soldier to die
- Develop literary skills by producing a diary

Prior knowledge

Students need to know that many soldiers, on both sides, died during the war. They should have some knowledge of the carnage of the Battle of the Somme, and understand how dangerous the trenches and the new weapons could be.

QCA links

Unit 18 Twentieth-century conflicts

NC links

History skills 2c, 2e, 5c
Breadth of study 13, the two world wars

Scottish attainment targets

Environmental Studies – Society – People in the past
Strand – The nature of historical evidence
Level C

Northern Ireland PoS

Study Unit 4: The twentieth-century world, a) The impact of world war, World War I
Study Units 5 and 6: c) A significant era or turning point in history, the First World War

Background

World War 1 had a devastating effect on the European population, as a whole generation of young men were killed in their prime. As a result, young women of marrying age outnumbered men in Britain, and this left many of them without partners. Many young women were left widowed by the war and were forced to bring up their families alone. However, nobody could have foreseen how long the war would last in 1914, and the new recruits to the armed forces did not realise that the odds of them returning unharmed to civilian life were stacked against them. The 'Over the Top!' game gives students a chance to 'experience' the war first-hand.

Starter activity

Use a quick fire quiz to remind students of all the key information they have learned about fighting in World War 1. Topics should include types of weapons, trench life and tactics used in battles such as the Somme.

Resource sheets and activity sheets

The 'Over the Top!' activity is designed to encourage students to empathise with the plight of British soldiers who fought in the war. Do not tell the students in advance that the game is weighted so that most of them will die during the war! Before the lessons, photocopy enough resources for the whole class. Some dice and coloured counters will also be needed. Photocopy and enlarge one 'War memorial' resource sheet and stick it to the class board. One game board is suitable for four to six players. Divide the class into groups. Each group will need the following: one game instruction sheet; one game board (fit the four 'Over the top! Game board' resource sheets together to create the game board – the dates should run consecutively from 1914 to 1918 around the outside edge; the board could be enlarged to A3 size); one set of game spinners copied onto coloured card (a sharpened pencil pushed through the middle makes a good spinner); one dice plus playing counters; each player will need a 'War diary' resource sheet; each player will need to use their 'character' from the 'Character card' resource sheet.

Read through the instructions carefully as a class and explain that the purpose of the game is to create our own unique war diary. As the students move around the board, they should log down where they are and what has happened to them. If they die, they should write their character's name on the class war memorial. The diary can lead on to a more descriptive written piece if desired.

Plenary

Select students at random. Ask them to tell you either one thing that they have learned from playing this game or one thing that has shocked them the most while playing this game.

Over the top! Game instructions

All players begin at the start square. Take turns to throw one dice and move the number of spaces on the board. Follow the instructions or directions given on the square that you land on. The object of the game is to get around the board and to Return to Blighty. The game finishes when the last player has completed the game. As you continue around the board, keep a war diary of your war experiences, including dates and events.

Christmas Truce

All players must stop here regardless of what they throw.

All Quiet on the Western Front

These are safe squares. If you land on one, you need take no further action on that turn.

Dice with Death

If you land on one of these squares, spin the DICE WITH DEATH spinner and follow the instructions. If you are sent to Hospital, go directly there and wait until your next turn to spin the HOSPITAL spinner.

Army Field Hospital

Spin the HOSPITAL spinner and follow the instructions.

Prisoner of War Camp

If you are sent to the PoW camp, you have two choices. You can opt to stay in the camp until the end of the war, or you can throw the dice on each of your turns while the other players are still playing. If you throw a six, you have escaped and can rejoin the war at the nearest All Quiet space from where you were captured.

Killed in a battle

If you are killed in battle, go straight to the Flanders Fields War Cemetery and follow the instructions given for the Cemetery below.

Flanders Fields War Cemetery

If you end up here, the war is definitely over for you. Put your character name on the class war memorial and the date that you died. You can now help the other players by reading out the instructions on the spinners.

Medical Discharge

The war is now over for you. You are home, but you cannot win the game. You can now help the other players by reading out the instructions on the spinners.

World War 1 © Folens (copiable page)

Over the top! Game spinners

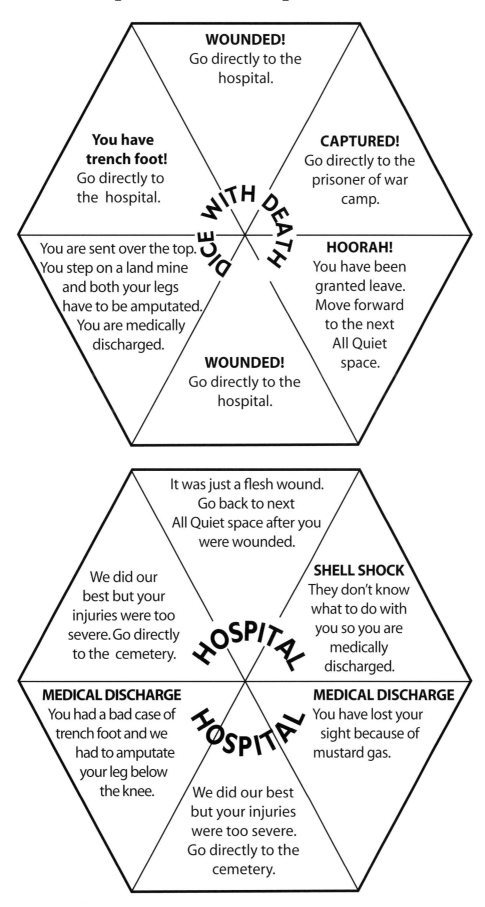

DICE WITH DEATH

WOUNDED!
Go directly to the hospital.

CAPTURED!
Go directly to the prisoner of war camp.

HOORAH!
You have been granted leave. Move forward to the next All Quiet space.

WOUNDED!
Go directly to the hospital.

You are sent over the top. You step on a land mine and both your legs have to be amputated. You are medically discharged.

You have trench foot!
Go directly to the hospital.

HOSPITAL HOSPITAL

It was just a flesh wound. Go back to next All Quiet space after you were wounded.

SHELL SHOCK
They don't know what to do with you so you are medically discharged.

MEDICAL DISCHARGE
You have lost your sight because of mustard gas.

We did our best but your injuries were too severe. Go directly to the cemetery.

MEDICAL DISCHARGE
You had a bad case of trench foot and we had to amputate your leg below the knee.

We did our best but your injuries were too severe. Go directly to the cemetery.

Over the top! Board game (1)

Over the top! Board game (2)

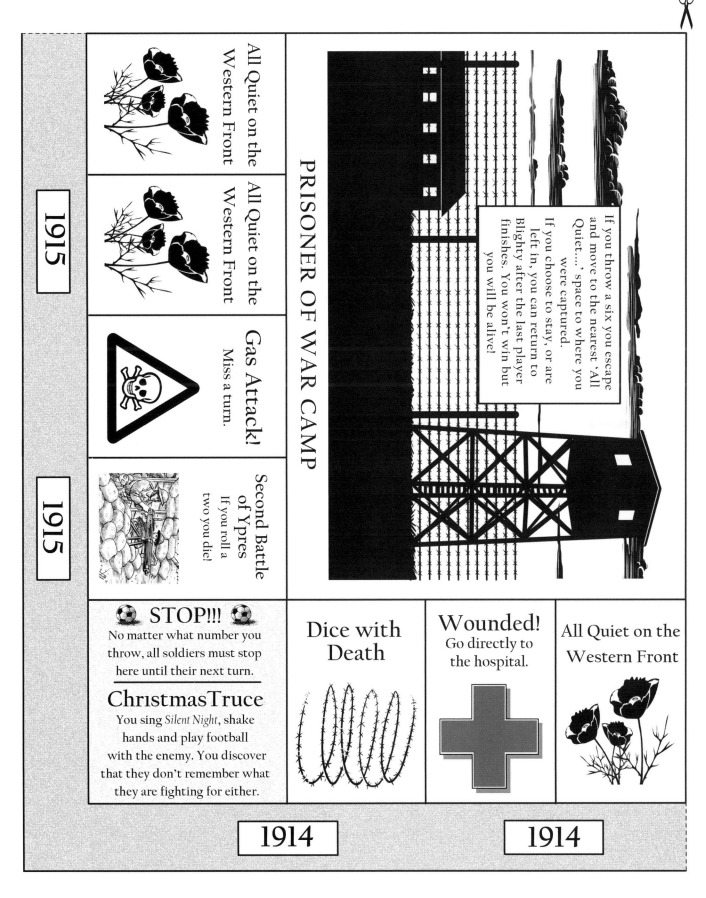

1915

All Quiet on the Western Front

1915

All Quiet on the Western Front

Gas Attack!
Miss a turn.

Second Battle of Ypres
If you roll a two you die!

PRISONER OF WAR CAMP

If you throw a six you escape and move to the nearest 'All Quiet...' space to where you were captured. If you choose to stay, or are left in, you can return to Blighty after the last player finishes. You won't win but you will be alive!

⚽ STOP!!! ⚽
No matter what number you throw, all soldiers must stop here until their next turn.

Christmas Truce
You sing *Silent Night*, shake hands and play football with the enemy. You discover that they don't remember what they are fighting for either.

Dice with Death

Wounded!
Go directly to the hospital.

All Quiet on the Western Front

1914

1914

Over The Top! Board game (3)

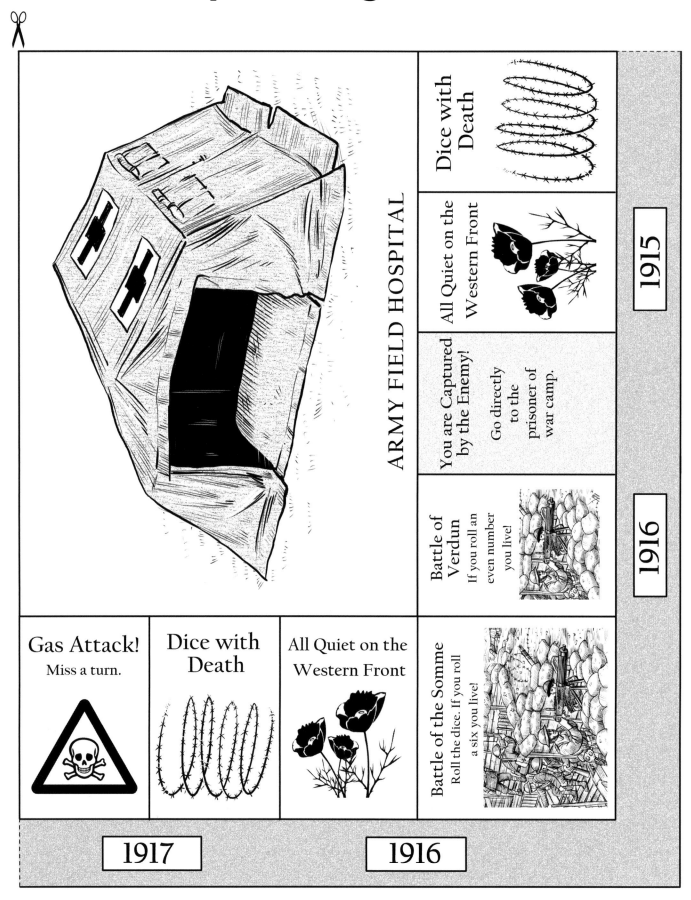

ARMY FIELD HOSPITAL

Dice with Death

All Quiet on the Western Front

You are Captured by the Enemy!

Go directly to the prisoner of war camp.

Battle of Verdun

If you roll an even number you live!

1915

1916

Gas Attack!

Miss a turn.

Dice with Death

All Quiet on the Western Front

Battle of the Somme

Roll the dice. If you roll a six you live!

1917

1916

Over the top! Board game (4)

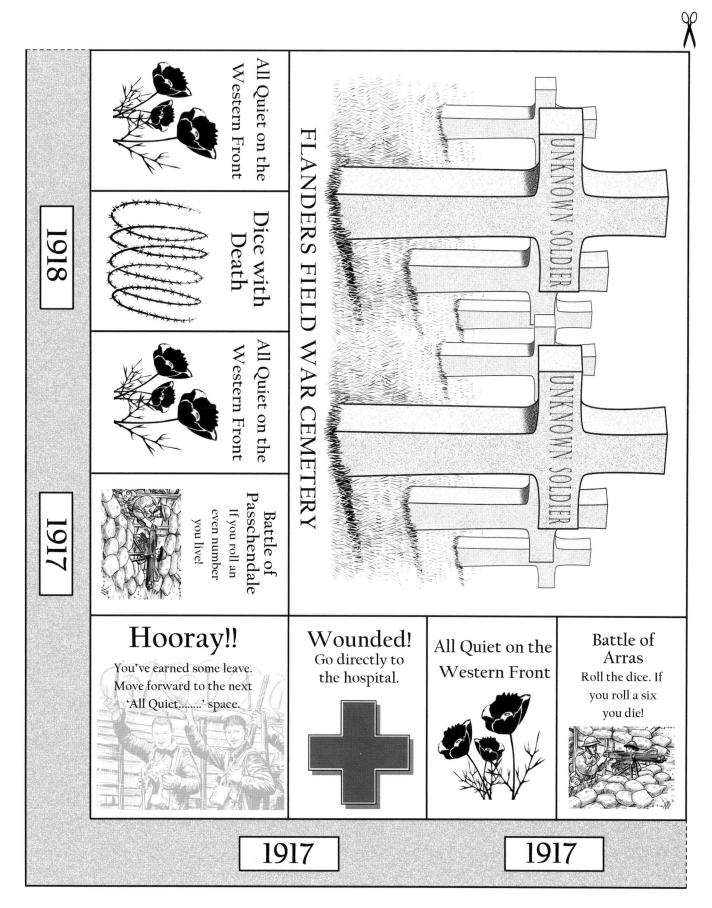

Over the top! War memorial

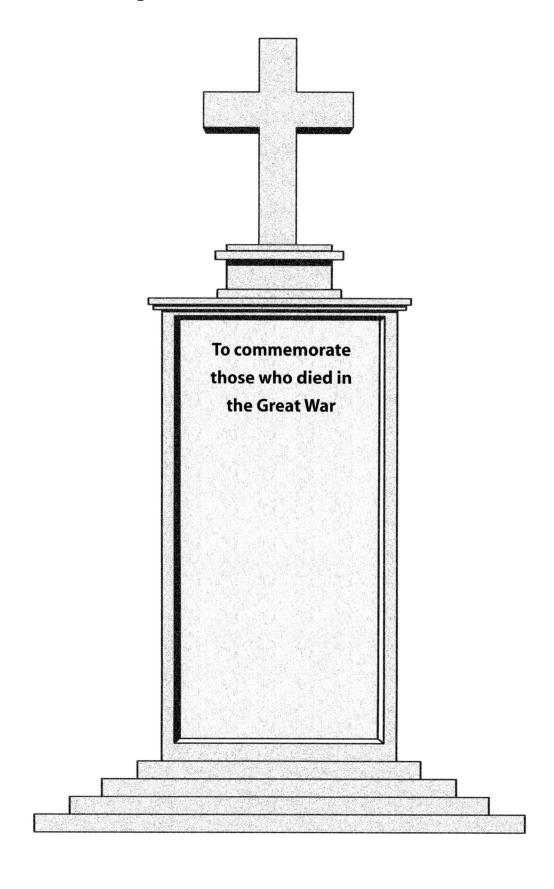

To commemorate
those who died in
the Great War

World War 1

Over the top! War diary

Character Name _____   Age _____

Date	Where did you go?	What happened to you and how did you feel?

Teacher's notes

What happened at the end of the war?

Objectives

- Understand that there was no clear winner of World War 1
- Understand how the role of women in society was beginning to change
- Identify reasons why the Treaty of Versailles angered Germany

Prior knowledge

Students need to know that the stalemate on the Western Front that had begun in 1914 was still in place at the beginning of 1918 and looked likely to continue.

QCA links

Unit 18 Twentieth-century conflicts

NC links

History skills 2c, 3a, 3b, 7a
Breadth of study 13, the two world wars

Scottish attainment targets

Strand – People, events and societies of significance in the past
Level E

Northern Ireland PoS

Study Unit 4: The twentieth-century world, a) The impact of world war, World War I
Study Units 5 and 6: c) A significant era or turning point in history, the First World War

Starter activity

Create a mind map that recaps the reasons why World War 1 started.

Resource sheets and activity sheet

'The steps to peace' provides a simplified version of the main reasons why the war came to an end in 1918. Explain clearly what an Armistice is, ensuring that the students are aware that it is not a surrender.

'How did the war end?' is a follow-on activity from 'The steps to peace'.

'What good did the war do?' revisits the topic of women's involvement in the war effort and the long-term changes that this helped to create.

Use 'Votes for women!' to help students explore the two sides of the argument on extending the franchise to women.

'Why was Germany angry?' looks at the Treaty of Versailles and asks students to examine why the imposed treaty was considered unfair. This activity also provides a good introduction to the rise of Hitler and Nazism, as well as introducing the idea that the origins of World War 2 were rooted in the end of World War 1.

Plenary

Ask students to write their own version of the Treaty of Versailles that could have led to lasting peace in Europe.

Background

By the end of 1917, the end of the war was nowhere in sight. There was still a stalemate on the Western Front and most of Europe was weary after many years of war. The series of events that led to the signing of the Armistice in November 1918 are very complicated. However, the most significant changes occurred because of internal political unrest in Russia, and then later in Germany. As a result, the ruling monarchs of both nations were replaced and this led in turn to a change of priorities for the new governments and a need to end their involvement in the war.

World War 1 © Folens

The steps to peace

At the end of 1917, there was still a **stalemate**. It looked as if the war would go on for another two years. However, things were about to change.

Russia, one of Britain's allies, had problems of its own. The people of Russia were having a revolution and could no longer fight on the **Eastern Front**. They signed a **treaty** with Germany to stop fighting in March 1918.

Germany decided that now they no longer needed to defend the **Eastern Front**, they could send all their soldiers to the **Western Front**. They hoped that this would help them to win the war. They started to prepare for the final battle.

The United States of America had formed an **alliance** with Britain. They sent a million troops to the **Western Front**. They also brought lots of weapons and tanks to help fight the Germans. But the German army was also well prepared. Anybody could win.

The German people were tired of war. They were starving because there were food shortages and people were dying. They forced Kaiser Wilhelm to give up the throne. Many German soldiers started to **surrender**. The leaders of the German army decided to give up. They agreed to sign an **armistice**. This was an agreement to end the war, which took place at 11 o'clock on 11 November 1918. After four years of fighting and eight million deaths, World War 1 was finally over!

How did the war end?

☞ Use the information on 'The steps to peace' resource sheet to answer the following questions. Write your answers in the spaces provided.

1 Why did Russia stop fighting in the war?

Russia stopped fighting in the war because _____

_____

_____

2 What was Germany going to do with all the soldiers from the Eastern Front now that they no longer had to fight the Russians?

Germany decided to _____

_____

_____

3 How many soldiers did the United States of America send to the Western Front to help the British?

_____

4 Why did Germany sign the armistice?

Germany signed the armistice because _____

_____

_____

5 Write a short definition of the following keywords.

Stalemate

_____

_____

Armistice

_____

_____

What good did the war do?

Before World War 1, many people believed that a woman's place was in the home. They thought that women were supposed to stay at home and look after the house and the children. They believed that only men should go out to work.

People did not believe that women were very good at running things outside the house. So before the war, only men had the right to make the laws or had the right to vote. Women called **suffragettes** tried to change things but the government would not listen to them.

When the war started, most of the men went off to fight for their country so there were not enough men left to do all the jobs that needed doing. The government had to get the women to go out to work. Women were soon doing all the jobs that the men had been doing, and they did a very good job too!

When the war finished, the government tried to make the women go back to their 'place' in the home. The women refused and argued that they were as good as men and should have the same rights that the men had. The government had to listen to them this time because they had proved that they were capable of doing the same things as men. Some women were given the vote in 1918, and by 1928, all women over the age of 21 were given the right to vote.

World War 1

Votes for women!

☞ Make a table in your book with two columns. One should be headed 'Reasons against votes for women' and the other should be headed 'Reasons in favour of votes for women'. Cut out and read the cards below carefully and decide which arguments you should stick into which column.

Children need their mothers at home to look after them.	Women helped to win the war as they made most of the weapons.	Women are more emotional so they cannot make difficult decisions.
The men returning from the war deserve to have their jobs back.	Men are much cleverer than women.	The children did not suffer when the women helped the war effort.
Women are just as clever as men.	Women are not prepared to be treated unfairly again.	Women must fill the places of all the men who were killed in the war.
The country is in a mess now that the war is over, so we must all try to fix it.	The women will stop marrying men and having children.	God made women to look after children and their husbands.

World War 1

Why was Germany angry?

After the war ended, all of Europe was in a mess. The war had destroyed many towns and factories. Many people were now very poor and they had to rebuild their lives and their countries.

In 1919, the countries that were involved in the war signed a treaty. This was a list of things that they all agreed to do so that the war would not start again. Many people in Europe blamed Germany for the war. They used the new treaty to punish Germany.

Treaty of Versailles

1   Germany is to blame for the war.

2   Germany must give all of its colonies to Britain and France.

3   Germany must get rid of most of its army and weapons.

4   Germany must pay millions of pounds to Britain and its allies.

☞ **Class discussion point**

Can you think of any reasons why Germany felt that the Treaty of Versailles was unfair?

☞ Use the information above and your discussion to make a list of reasons why Germany thought that the Treaty of Versailles was unfair.

Germany thought that the Treaty of Versailles was unfair because:

1 _____

2 _____

3 _____

4 _____

5 _____

Assessment sheet – World War I

☑ Tick the boxes to show what you know.

I know:	Yes	Not sure	Don't know
why the war started			
what a trench was like			
why men joined the army to fight in the war			
what different weapons were used in the war			
why so many died at the Battle of the Somme			
how the government censored the news			
why some soldiers were against the war			
why the government needed women to go to work			
how difficult it would have been to survive the war			
how the war ended			
why Germany was angry about the Treaty of Versailles			

One thing that I remember most about this topic is:

_____

_____

I would like to learn more about:

_____

_____